A Souvenir
and Guide to

THE ROYAL BOTANIC
GARDENS, KEW

LONDON: HMSO

Right. Tropical rainforest - an endangered ecosystem that is a storehouse of genetic diversity

THE ROLE OF THE
ROYAL BOTANIC GARDENS, KEW

The mission of the Royal Botanic Gardens, Kew, is to ensure better management of the Earth's environment by increasing our knowledge and understanding of the plant kingdom: the basis of life on Earth.

Our mission will be achieved through worldwide research into plants and the ecosystem, publication, access to all knowledge so gained for the world's scientific community and through the display and interpretation to the public of the collections at Kew and Wakehurst Place.

Whenever possible, the Royal Botanic Gardens, Kew, will endeavour to reduce and reverse the rate of destruction of the world's plant species and their habitats.

Right. Princess Augusta
Centre right. William Aiton
Far right. William Chambers

The Royal Botanic Gardens, Kew, consist mainly of two estates which originally belonged to the Royal family. In 1759, Augusta, Dowager Princess of Wales and mother of George III, laid out 3 $\frac{1}{2}$ ha of her estate as a botanic garden. William Aiton became her head gardener, Lord Bute her botanical adviser and Sir William Chambers, the architect, designed a number of buildings for the botanic garden and surrounding pleasure grounds.

On Augusta's death in 1772, George III combined his grandfather's neighbouring Richmond estate with that of Kew. Sir Joseph Banks became the unofficial director and the fame of the botanic garden is largely due to him. It was at his instigation that collectors were sent out all over the world in pursuit of plants of economic, scientific or horticultural interest.

Above. Kew in Victorian times

Far left. Sir Joseph Banks

Left. Sir William Hooker

Right. The Pagoda, designed by Sir William Chambers for Princess Augusta

In 1840, after a period of decline, the botanic garden was handed over to the State, and in the following year Sir William Hooker was appointed the first official director. The Museums and Department of Economic Botany (1847) and the Herbarium and Library (1852) were all established by Sir William; the Jodrell Laboratory was opened in 1876 when his son, Sir Joseph Hooker, was director. During the last century, the Royal family relinquished large parts of their estates to the botanic gardens, which are now just over 121 ha in extent. The collection has also grown in size from the small beginnings of Augusta's botanic garden to a current total of over 30,000 different types of plants.

Formerly part of the Ministry of Agriculture, Fisheries and Food (MAFF), the Royal Botanic Gardens became a corporate body with charitable status and a Board of Trustees under the provisions of the National Heritage Act 1983. It is primarily funded by direct government grant via MAFF, but is also supported by the Royal Botanic Gardens, Kew, Foundation and the Friends of the Royal Botanic Gardens, Kew.

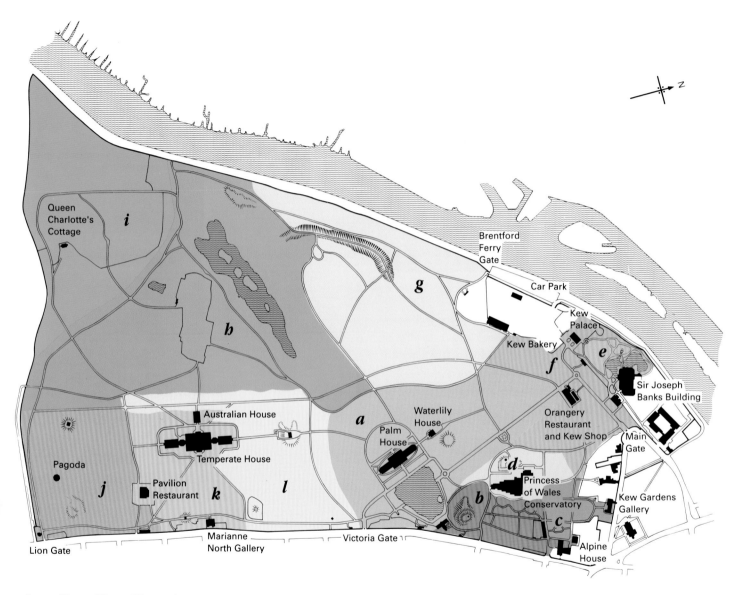

Queen
Charlotte's
Cottage

i

b

g

Brentford
Ferry
Gate

Car Park

Kew
Palace

Kew Bakery

f

e

Sir Joseph
Banks Building

Australian House

Waterlily
House

a

Palm
House

Orangery
Restaurant
and Kew Shop

Main
Gate

Temperate House

Pagoda

j

Pavilion
Restaurant

k

l

d

Princess
of Wales
Conservatory

b

Kew Gardens
Gallery

c

Lion Gate

Marianne
North Gallery

Victoria Gate

Alpine
House

| 0 | 100 | 200 | 300 | yards |
| 0 | 100 | 200 | 300 | metres |

INTRODUCTION

A botanic garden is an ordered collection of plants, assembled primarily for scientific and educational purposes. The Royal Botanic Gardens, Kew, is in effect an encyclopaedia of living and preserved plants, a garden and a green laboratory.

In response to the developing environmental crisis, scientists from the Gardens are cataloguing the incredible diversity of the tropical regions: areas such as the rainforests contain 90,000 of the world's 250,000 known flowering plants. We are now screening many of these for their potential medicinal value or assessing them as new crops. Endangered plants (some reduced to only one or two individuals) are being propagated for distribution to other botanic gardens and, wherever possible, eventual re-introduction into the wild.

The combination of horticultural, technical and conservation expertise existing in the Gardens has created a wonderful amenity. The beautifully laid-out garden areas and the rich displays in our glasshouses provide endless pleasure and interest for all our visitors.

PALM HOUSE

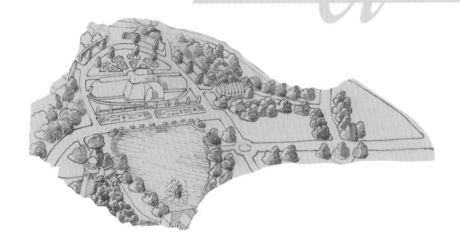

Below. Rubber (*Hevea brasiliensis*) seeds

Right. The Palm House, seen from the top of the Campanile

Set in an area of formal bedding, the Palm House provides a Victorian centre-piece to the Gardens. The building stands at the hub of a series of dramatic vistas designed by William Nesfield (1793-1881). Towards the Orangery is the Broad Walk with its spectacular seasonal plantings, whilst to the south the Pagoda can be glimpsed through the trees. To the west, a vista leads the eye across the Thames to Syon House.

The Palm House was also the focal point for the great nineteenth-century botanic garden; within its graceful confines, the plant wealth of the tropical world was displayed to an amazed Victorian public. Both dramatic and elegant, the curvilinear structure of the Palm House is a classic example of Victorian design - the result of a collaboration between the architect, Decimus Burton, and the engineer, Richard Turner. Constructed between 1844 and 1848, it was designed to house tropical trees and shrubs, in particular the palms. One hundred and forty years of heat and condensation had reduced the building to a dangerous state and, as a result, it was closed to the public in 1984. The

plant collections were moved to temporary growing quarters and, between 1984 and 1989, the House was almost completely dismantled and rebuilt, using the original materials and specifications where possible. At the same time, changes were made to improve the growing conditions for plants.

There are many interesting plants to be seen in this splendid house. Several of the economically important plants displayed have historical connections with the Gardens, notably rubber (*Hevea brasiliensis*) and breadfruit (*Artocarpus altilis*). In contrast to these widely grown crops, the cycads are amongst the world's rarest and most ancient plant species; many are now on the verge of extinction in their natural habitats.

Right. Miniature coral reef in the Marine Display

The Palm House contains plants from two of the world's most species-diverse ecosystems, the tropical rainforest and the tropical seas. Until recently, we were unable to display marine plants, but new techniques have been developed to enable the cultivation of this difficult plant group. A series of tanks beneath the Palm House displays plants from many habitats including tropical mangrove swamps and European tidal rock pools.

Right. *Diplocyclos palmatus* can be seen in the Waterlily House

THE TULIP TREE -
Liriodendron tulipifera

The name of this distinctive hardy tree refers to the unusual tulip-shaped flowers which are produced in June and July. Its leaves are characteristically cut across at the tip: according to legend this is due to the Devil taking a bite out of the leaf when in a rage!

*The tulip tree was one of the first introductions to Europe from eastern North America in the seventeenth century. The rarer Chinese tulip tree (**L. chinense**) was not discovered until 1875. Closely related to magnolias, tulip trees represent the fragments of a once widespread prehistoric vegetation disrupted by the Ice Ages.*

To the north of the Palm House stands the Waterlily House (No. 15), designed by Richard Turner and constructed in 1852. It was originally built to house the giant Amazonian waterlily (*Victoria amazonica*), which is now grown in the Princess of Wales Conservatory. The Waterlily House holds the sacred lotus (*Nelumbo nucifera*) and the papyrus (*Cyperus papyrus*) as well as a collection of tropical waterlilies and other aquatics. Against the inner walls of this hot steamy house grow a variety of tropical climbers, including some bizarre members of the cucumber family such as the bottle gourd (*Lagenaria siceraria*) and the loofah (*Luffa cylindrica*).

In front of the Palm House is the Palm House Pond, overlooked by the former Museum of Economic Botany, also designed by Decimus Burton. The pond is dominated by the fountain and statue of Hercules and Achelous, the latter being a favoured perch for fishing herons on quiet evenings. Behind the Palm House, the formal rose gardens are at their peak in early to mid-summer.

HERBACEOUS AREA

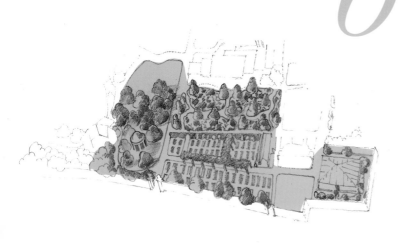

On the southern edge of the Herbaceous Area is the Temple of Aeolus, designed by Sir William Chambers in 1760 and rebuilt by Decimus Burton in 1845. It has a prominent and enchanting position on the Cumberland Mound, overlooking both the Palm House Pond and the Woodland Garden.

The Woodland Garden is laid out to represent the change in vegetation between forest and alpine zones and consists, as in nature, of three layers. The deciduous tree canopy of oaks (*Quercus*) and birches (*Betula*) supports climbers and provides shade for the layer below. Rhododendrons, maples (*Acer*) and other choice deciduous shrubs act as a foil to such ground-cover plants as hellebores (*Helleborus*), primulas, Himalayan blue poppies *(Meconopsis betonicifolia)* and the spectacular North American trilliums.

Left. *Tropaeolum speciosum*, a
climber in the Woodland Garden

Right. Christmas rose,
Helleborus niger

Below. Himalayan blue poppy,
Meconopsis betonicifolia

13

Left. *Eryngium bourgatii*
in the family Umbelliferae

Below. Squirting cucumber,
Ecballium elaterium

Order Beds

In the sixteenth century, it was common for medicinal plants to be laid out systematically by plant family so that medical students could easily recognise and identify them. A similar idea in the form of the Order Beds was used by Sir Joseph Hooker to teach students of botany and horticulture how to recognise flowering plants. This process of recognising, identifying, naming and understanding the relationships between plants is known as taxonomy. This science is the basis of all work carried out on plants and is one of the main parts of our scientific research.

The Order Beds provide the keen gardener with a rich and varied arrangement of herbaceous plants. They house such beauties as the poppies *(Papaver)*, evening primroses (*Oenothera*) and peonies (*Paeonia*) as well as the mandrake (*Mandragora*), squirting cucumbers (*Ecballium elaterium*) and other unusual plants. A pergola covered with sweet-scented climbing roses covers the central path, and walls around part of the garden shelter many interesting and attractive plants, for example *Actinidia kolomikta* with its pink and green early summer foliage.

14

Rock Garden

Originally constructed in 1882 out of limestone to resemble a Pyrenean mountain valley, this lovely garden has been altered over the last sixty years to allow more imaginative landscaping and the cultivation of plants with special needs. The site, which is more than half a hectare in extent, is made up of a number of outcrops of Sussex sandstone, chosen for its moisture retention and cooling effect on the surrounding plants.

Within the Rock Garden, peat gullies and other special environments have been created to house plants such as the Irish heath (*Daboecia cantabrica*). Water features with damp marginal areas allow the cultivation of globe flowers (*Trollius*), kingcups (*Caltha*) and other moisture-loving plants. Although we try whenever possible to grow plants of wild origin, the Rock Garden displays a wide range of specimens from various sources, from the common garden aubrietia to the rare *Daphne rodreguesii*.

15

Right. The mountain region
of the Aletsch Glacier in the
Swiss Alps

Far right. Alpine plants -

Top. *Leucanthemopsis alpina*
ssp. *alpina*

Upper centre. *Sempervivum
arachnoideum*

Lower centre. *Ranunculus
weberbaueri*

Bottom. *Gentiana brachyphylla*

Alpine House

The Alpine House, opened in 1981, is pyramidal in design and is both practical and imaginative, with much of its area landscaped to provide a permanent display. Inside the house alpine plants from the Southern Hemisphere and equatorial mountain areas, along with small tender Mediterranean plants such as those from the Balearic Islands, are sheltered from excessive wet and severe frosts. The more traditionally grown alpine plants and bulbs are placed in plunge areas and a show bench, forming a display that can be changed at intervals. Colour is maintained throughout the year by selecting species with different flowering requirements from our large and diverse collection of plants from all over the world, which is grown 'behind the scenes'.

16

Left. *Pulsatilla vulgaris*
Left below. *Phlox subulata*
Below. The Alpine House

The central refrigerated bench holds plants from the Arctic and high montane equatorial regions. Their exacting environmental requirements are met by careful control of soil temperature and light. In the Arctic section, primulas and poppies (*Papaver*) are grown, while the equatorial mountain zone includes various giant alpines, such as lobelias, puyas and espeletias, their large size being an adaptation to the extreme conditions in which the plants normally grow.

Outside the house are general rock features, raised beds, peat-loving plants and tufa beds.

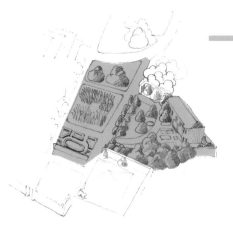

AQUATIC GARDEN AND
GRASS GARDEN

W ith the destruction of wetland habitats throughout the world, once-common aquatics, water-margin and marsh plants are becoming increasingly rare.

The Aquatic Garden, first laid out in 1909, provides a variety of wet conditions for some of these plants. The large central pool holds a selection of summer-flowering waterlilies (*Nuphar*, *Nymphaea* etc) whilst the four smaller corner pools contain reed maces (*Typha*), bulrushes (*Schoenoplectus lacustris*) and the brandy bottle (*Nuphar lutea*) as well as other interesting specimens. Long side beds show representatives of British marsh plants including such curiosities as the spiral juncus (*Juncus effusus* var. *spiralis*) and the now scarce ragged robin (*Lychnis flos-cuculi*).

Right. *Nymphaea* 'Sirius'

Right. *Phalaris aquatica*
Far right. The Grass Garden

Close by, the Grass Garden provides interest throughout the year, but in autumn its plantings of grasses that are important for both agriculture and horticulture are especially fascinating. Two central beds show cereals from temperate and subtropical zones, including primitive and present day cultivars of wheat (*Triticum*) as well as maize (*Zea mays*) and millets (for example, *Pennisetum*). Among the many grasses hardy in the British Isles, some of the most attractive and unusual ornamental species are the mosquito grass (*Bouteloua gracilis*) and the quaking grass (*Briza maxima*). A series of brick-edged beds nearby display lawn turf suited to particular purposes.

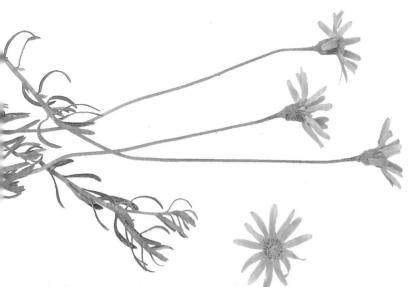

Left. *Felicia amoena*

Right. Cambridge Cottage now houses the Kew Gardens Gallery

Below. *Glaucium phoenicum*

Cambridge Cottage and Duke's Garden

To the north of the Grass Garden is the attractive Duke's Garden, with Cambridge Cottage forming a pleasant backdrop and providing an elegant setting for the Kew Gardens Gallery. Formerly the residence of the Duke of Cambridge, the house and its grounds were bequeathed to the Gardens in 1904. The building was initially used as a Wood Museum, but now displays exhibitions of botanical illustrations and flower paintings, some of which are for sale.

The Duke's Garden is planted so that there is something to see all year round. In the seclusion of this walled area, a selection of blue-flowered, grey-leaved and variegated specimens form borders to the lawned area containing informal island beds. These are rich in colourful herbaceous plants. Notable specimens include plume poppies (*Macleaya cordata*), cleomes, clematis and many members of the daisy and mint families (Compositae and Labiatae), renowned for their late summer colour.

Just outside the garden, the south side of the wall shelters the Duchess Border. Acting in part as an experimental area to select plants for hardiness, it contains many unusual plants from such areas as South Africa, Tasmania, Mexico and New Zealand, the latter country providing the spectacular *Sophora microphylla*. Beyond this strip and to the west stands the magnificent stone pine (*Pinus pinea*), a popular feature in the Gardens for over 150 years.

PRINCESS OF WALES
CONSERVATORY

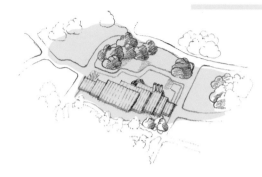

Right. Lush vegetation in the moist tropical zone

Below. Aerial view of the Princess of Wales Conservatory

Named, by consent of the Queen, in honour of the present Princess of Wales, the Conservatory's title also recognises her Royal predecessor, Augusta. This new conservatory makes use of the latest technology available for glasshouse environmental control and has extended the range of plants which are on view. Its innovative design allows efficient and cost-effective management of several habitats under one roof as well as expansion of the scientific collections, so necessary with our increasing involvement in plant conservation.

Ten climatic zones are maintained within the building, ranging from arid to moist tropical. Within the hot and humid area, mangrove swamp and riverine habitats display typical vegetation, such as the giant Amazonian waterlily (*Victoria amazonica*) and the water hyacinth (*Eichhornia crassipes*), renowned for its rapid spread and clogging of inland waterways. Also present are several important useful plants originating in the wet tropics, including banana (*Musa*), sugar cane (*Saccharum officinarum*), cassava (*Manihot esculenta*) and pineapple (*Ananas sativus*).

In contrast, the arid zone houses plants tolerant of desert conditions, particularly the cacti and other succulents. Many of these plants are also very useful, such as *Aloe vera*, myrrh (*Commiphora*), sisal (*Agave sisalana*) and prickly pear (*Opuntia*). Orchids, ferns, savannah and cloud forest plants, along with carnivorous species and representative vegetation from endangered island habitats also form part of the exciting display in the Conservatory.

THE GIANT WATERLILY - *Victoria amazonica*

This huge aquatic plant, native to tropical South America, was first discovered in Guyana in 1837, and subsequently named in honour of Queen Victoria. Its enormous leaves, which can measure over 2 m in diameter, are supported below by a network of inflated ribs. A mature leaf can support 45 kg if the load is evenly distributed.

Treated as an annual here and raised from seed each year, the plant grows rapidly after the seedling is planted out in April. The flowers, appearing in mid-summer, are large and fragrant, but last only forty-eight hours. They change colour as they mature, from white through pink to purplish red.

Above. Arrows coated with poison made from *Strophanthus* seeds, which are also the source of a heart drug

Below. Raspberry, *Rubus idaeus* 'Autumn Bliss'

Right. The glass-covered concourse of the Sir Joseph Banks Building

Near to both the Main Gate and Kew Palace, the Sir Joseph Banks Building and its surrounding landscape offer an exciting new experience to our visitors. This innovative earth-covered building, with its special energy-conservation heating systems, houses the outstanding Economic Botany collection and library and a large exhibition hall. The hall is devoted to a series of spectacular exhibitions showing how much we depend on the plant world and why, therefore, the conservation of plant habitats and the management of the Earth's resources is so vital to our future.

Both the interior plantings of the building's conservatory area and the exterior landscaped beds continue the theme of 'Plants for People'. Trees such as pines (*Pinus*) and eucalyptus provide examples of sources of timber and pulp for the production of cellulose, which is used for items as diverse as viscose fabric and spectacle frames. Other useful plants include soft fruits, herbs and a variety of medicinal plants, such as *Ephedra* which is incorporated into some hay fever remedies.

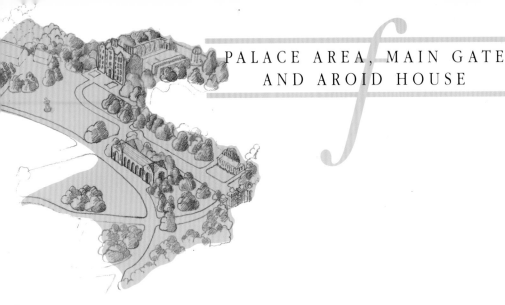

Beyond the imposing wrought-iron Main Gates, designed by Decimus Burton in 1845, the Broad Walk, edged by formal bedding and several spectacular late-flowering Indian horse chestnuts (*Aesculus indica*), leads out into the Gardens. Among the trees planted in the areas on either side of the Broad Walk are several remaining from Princess Augusta's botanic garden. One notable example is the maidenhair tree (*Ginkgo biloba*), with its vibrant yellow autumn colour, which is named because its leaves resemble a maidenhair fern in shape. To one side stands the Aroid House, the oldest glasshouse at Kew, which was originally sited in the grounds of Buckingham Palace. At the direction of William IV, it was moved to Kew in 1836 and modified by Jeffry Wyatville. Until recently it housed a spectacular collection of tropical plants, many of which are economically important. It is now awaiting restoration and will be used as a visitor centre.

Right. Maidenhair tree, *Ginkgo biloba*

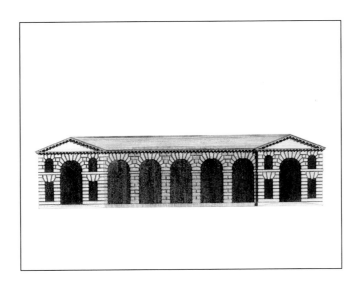

Left. Sir William Chambers'
drawing of the Orangery

Orangery

The Orangery, built in 1761, is perhaps one of the most beautiful of Sir William Chambers' designs. It is sited within the right angle formed by the two sections of the Broad Walk. Although it was originally conceived as a place to keep tender evergreen plants, the moisture required for their growth caused severe damage to the structure and the plants themselves never flourished. The building was later used to house timbers, cabinet and furniture woods from the Great Exhibition of 1862.

Following a complete refurbishment programme, this lovely building now holds Kew's shop and a restaurant. A wide selection of items of botanical and horticultural interest are for sale, together with many gifts and souvenirs. There is also an audio-visual display on the work of the Gardens.

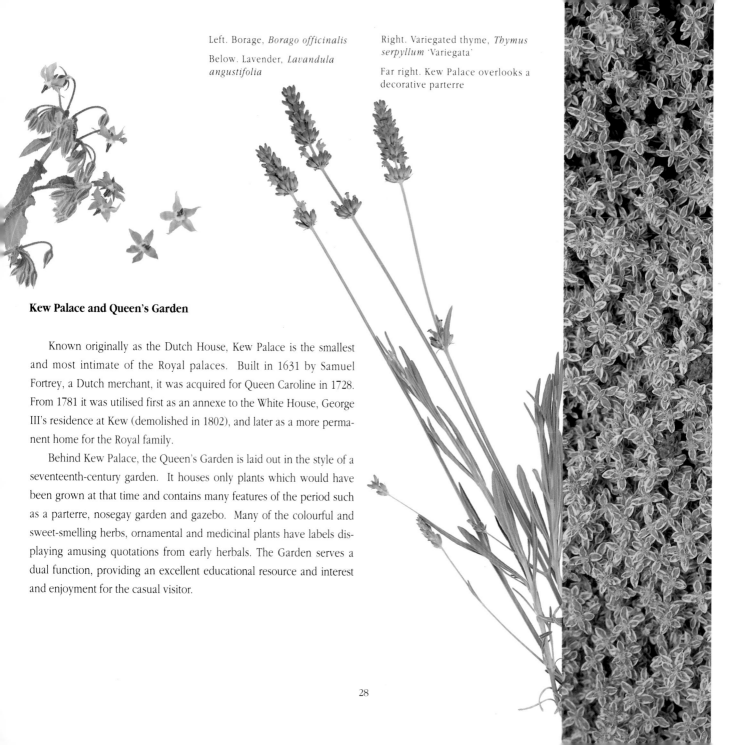

Left. Borage, *Borago officinalis*

Below. Lavender, *Lavandula angustifolia*

Right. Variegated thyme, *Thymus serpyllum* 'Variegata'

Far right. Kew Palace overlooks a decorative parterre

Kew Palace and Queen's Garden

Known originally as the Dutch House, Kew Palace is the smallest and most intimate of the Royal palaces. Built in 1631 by Samuel Fortrey, a Dutch merchant, it was acquired for Queen Caroline in 1728. From 1781 it was utilised first as an annexe to the White House, George III's residence at Kew (demolished in 1802), and later as a more permanent home for the Royal family.

Behind Kew Palace, the Queen's Garden is laid out in the style of a seventeenth-century garden. It houses only plants which would have been grown at that time and contains many features of the period such as a parterre, nosegay garden and gazebo. Many of the colourful and sweet-smelling herbs, ornamental and medicinal plants have labels displaying amusing quotations from early herbals. The Garden serves a dual function, providing an excellent educational resource and interest and enjoyment for the casual visitor.

BRENTFORD GATE, RHODODENDRON DELL AND BAMBOO GARDEN

Below. *Rhododendron fulgens*, one of many rhododendrons collected by Sir Joseph Hooker

In the north-western parts of the gardens, near the Brentford Gate, are some of the most attractive areas of seasonal interest. By January, the first rhododendrons are flowering and, if the winter is mild, the glorious carmine blooms of *Magnolia campbellii* appear. From mid-May until late June, lilacs (*Syringa*), azaleas, rhododendrons and magnolias dominate the area.

Excavated in 1773 by a company of Staffordshire Militia under the direction of 'Capability' Brown, the area now called Rhododendron Dell runs parallel to the River Thames. Within its shelter, and in the shade of many tall oak trees (*Quercus*), is a large collection of rhododendrons.

Adjacent to the Dell is the Bamboo Garden, a garden with interest throughout the year. Here, the graceful stems and leaves of the bamboos contrast with the coarse but exotic fan-like leaves of the Chusan palm (*Trachycarpus fortunei*).

Right. Bamboo, *Phyllostachys makinoi*

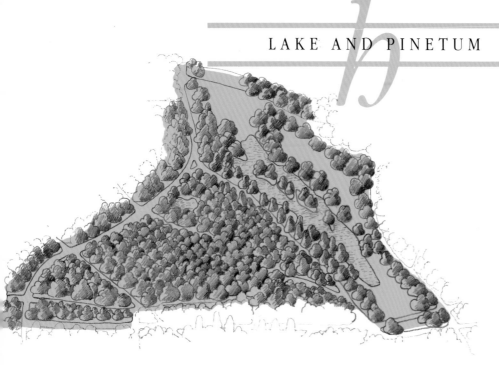

Above. *Cupressus dupreziana*

The area between the Lake and the Cottage Grounds is planted with a collection of conifers. These trees dominate the northern forests of Europe, America and Asia, which are some of the world's most important timber-producing areas.

Many conifers are adapted to withstand harsh environmental conditions; the northern species with their small leaves are resistant to winter cold and drought whilst the giant redwood (*Sequoiadendron giganteum*) of California has spongy bark that enables it to survive forest fires. One conifer grown here, *Cupressus dupreziana*, comes from the remote mountains of the Sahara Desert and has adapted to extreme water shortage. Within the collection is a number of conifers from the temperate regions of South America, probably the most bizarre being the monkey puzzle trees (*Araucaria araucana*) on the southern side of the Lake.

The Lake, which is artificial, has many moisture-loving trees and shrubs along its margins. An interesting adaptation to a waterlogged environment is shown by the swamp cypresses (*Taxodium*) which have stilt roots allowing air to reach the underground roots even when the trees are growing in the thick mud of their native Louisiana swamps.

On the Lake and the surrounding lawns is an extensive collection of ornamental waterfowl. Some of the birds, such as the beautifully plumaged mandarin duck (*Aix galericulata*), are part of a breeding collection held here. Many of our visiting wildfowl, notably the pochards (*Aythya ferina*) and tufted ducks (*A. fuligula*) are welcome; less so are the large and aggressive Canada geese (*Branta canadensis*) which compete with the more timid birds.

Above. Yellow iris, *Iris pseudacorus*

Right. The Lake

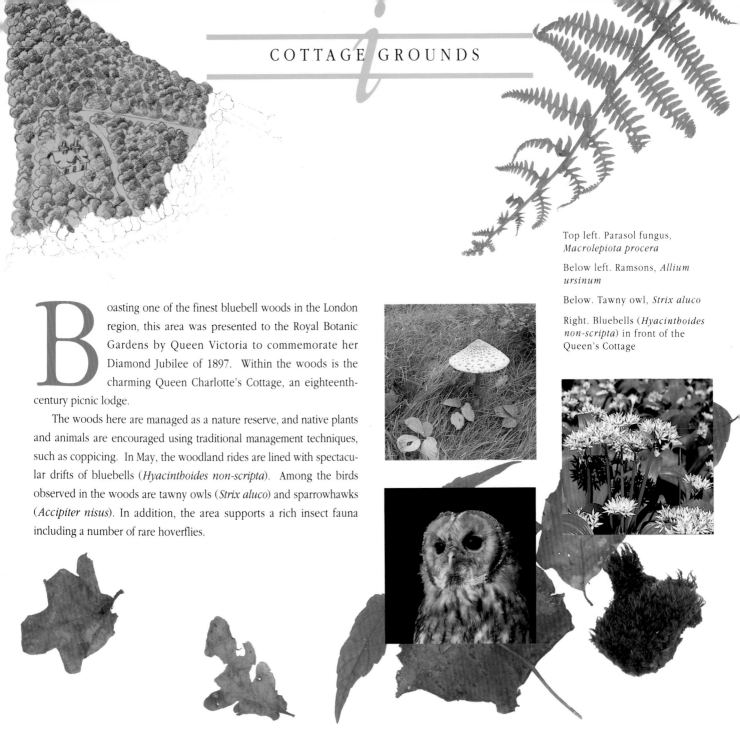

COTTAGE GROUNDS

Top left. Parasol fungus, *Macrolepiota procera*

Below left. Ramsons, *Allium ursinum*

Below. Tawny owl, *Strix aluco*

Right. Bluebells (*Hyacinthoides non-scripta*) in front of the Queen's Cottage

Boasting one of the finest bluebell woods in the London region, this area was presented to the Royal Botanic Gardens by Queen Victoria to commemorate her Diamond Jubilee of 1897. Within the woods is the charming Queen Charlotte's Cottage, an eighteenth-century picnic lodge.

The woods here are managed as a nature reserve, and native plants and animals are encouraged using traditional management techniques, such as coppicing. In May, the woodland rides are lined with spectacular drifts of bluebells (*Hyacinthoides non-scripta*). Among the birds observed in the woods are tawny owls (*Strix aluco*) and sparrowhawks (*Accipiter nisus*). In addition, the area supports a rich insect fauna including a number of rare hoverflies.

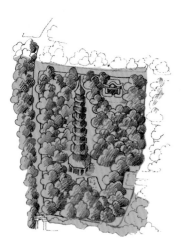

PAGODA

j

I t may no longer be a 'surprise' to discover a pagoda in the world's most famous botanic gardens, but that was its original intention, a 'surprise' for Princess Augusta. Built between 1761 and 1762, the Pagoda was designed by Sir William Chambers and is probably the best known of Kew's buildings. Standing at the end of Pagoda Vista, an avenue lined with paired trees of imposing stature including Caucasian elms (*Zelkova carpinifolia*) and sweet chestnuts (*Castanea sativa*), this ten-storey octagonal structure rises to over 50 m. It is a memorial to Chambers' interest in Chinese architecture, following his earlier visit to that country.

The Pagoda provides a focal point for the tranquil southern section of the Gardens. Nearby, the Heath Garden gives a colourful display even in winter, with a profusion of seasonal heathers such as cultivated varieties of *Erica herbacea* and *E.* x *darleyensis*. In contrast, summer flowering kurume azaleas (*Rhododendron*) landscape the area immediately to the west of the Pagoda, complementing the 'Chokushi-Mon' or Japanese Gateway.

Below left. *Erica cinerea* 'C. D. Eason'

Below. Sweet chestnuts, *Castanea sativa*

Right. The Pagoda

The Temperate House holds a rich and dramatic collection of plants from the subtropical areas of the world. The largest in volume of our glasshouses, it was designed by Decimus Burton and built in stages between 1860 and 1899. It was renovated and relandscaped between 1978 and 1982.

The house is planted in a geographical arrangement: the northern wing contains species from temperate Asia; the north octagon has plants from New Zealand and the Pacific Islands; the south octagon contains a collection of South African heaths (*Erica*) and proteas; and in the south wing are Mediterranean and African plants. In the central area, the effect is one of an arboretum under glass, with many tall subtropical trees and palms from around the world.

Two sections are of particular interest; one contains island plants and the other, economic plants. Many island plants are faced with imminent extinction due to competition from more aggressive alien introduced species. These endangered plants are grown and propagated at Kew for eventual re-introduction to the wild if conditions allow. Of the collection of economic plants, the jojoba (*Simmondsia chinensis*) is one of the newer arid-land crops that has become familiar from its use in shampoo and cosmetics in recent years. A continuing worldwide research programme is examining a wide variety of plant species in the search for economically valuable crops.

Left. *Erica hebecalyx*
Right. Inside the Temperate House

CHILEAN WINE PALM - *Jubaea chilensis*

One of the most impressive plants in Kew, this specimen was raised in 1846 from seed collected in Chile. It now measures over 17 m and threatens ultimately to grow through the roof of the Temperate House!

The palm originated from the slopes of the Andes in Chile where it is threatened by being tapped for its sweet sap. Although rare in the wild, the Chilean wine palm is widely grown in many subtropical areas as an ornamental tree.

Australian House

The Australian House, next to the Temperate House, contains a sample of the island continent's spectacular plant diversity. Built in 1952, the structure of the house is made from aluminium. Among the many plants in this house is one species of international interest, the Moreton Bay chestnut (*Castanospermum australe*). Work in the Garden's Jodrell Laboratory has identified this plant as having a potential role in the treatment of viral diseases such as AIDS.

Left. *Eucalyptus drummondii*

Centre left. Inside the
Australian House

Below left. *Callistemon subulatus*

Marianne North Gallery

Paintings of many Australian and other plants can be seen in the nearby Marianne North Gallery. Miss North was an intrepid Victorian traveller and painter who visited most parts of the world in order to depict the natural vegetation. The Gallery, which she presented to the Gardens in 1882, holds 832 of her oil paintings. To the south of the Gallery is the Ruined Arch, a mock ruin designed by Sir William Chambers in 1759.

Above right. The Australian plants, *Banksia coccinea* and the climbing *Gompholobium polymorphum*, painted by Marianne North

Right. Inside the Marianne North Gallery

KING WILLIAM'S TEMPLE, HOLLY WALK, BERBERIS DELL AND FLAG POLE

Below. *Berberis* x *stenophylla*
Right. Temple of Bellona

Holly Walk, lined with different cultivars of holly (*Ilex*), extends northwards from the Temperate House, following part of a route originally called Love Lane. To the east of this walk is King William's Temple, surrounded by a garden of predominantly Mediterranean plants. On a hot summer day, this area is redolent with the scents of aromatic shrubs such as lavender (*Lavandula*) and rosemary (*Rosmarinus*).

Visible from most areas of the Gardens is the Flag Pole, the fourth to be given to us. This was a gift from the British Columbia Loggers' Association and is made from a single piece of Douglas fir (*Pseudotsuga menziesii*). Nearby is the Berberis Dell which houses a collection of many species of berberis and the related mahonias.

Close to the Victoria Gate is the Temple of Bellona, built in 1760 and recently restored. It overlooks two highlights of the Kew year; in spring the nearby lawns are covered in spectacular drifts of crocus (over one and a half million were planted in 1987) whilst in autumn the old cotinus tree near the Temple turns a glorious red.

Top left. Endangered plant species are multiplied by micro-propagation

Bottom left. Plants are identified, named and classified in the Herbarium

Below. Studies of plant structure in the Jodrell Laboratory

The displays of plants in the glasshouses, beds and arboretum constitute only a small part of the work of the Gardens. Many newly collected endangered plants are held in nurseries where they are tended and propagated.

Also behind the scenes, the scientific research of the Gardens goes on. In the Herbarium, with its collection of some 6 million preserved specimens, botanists continue the vital task of identifying and naming plants from around the world. Complementing this research, scientists in the Jodrell Laboratory study plant chemistry and structure, both as an aid to plant identification and to investigate their potential economic value.